The Juice Bar

Sara Lewis

LOVE FOOD™

This edition published by Parragon Books Ltd in 2013

LOVE FOOD is an imprint of Parragon Books Ltd

Parragon Books Ltd
Chartist House, 15 – 17 Trim Street
Bath, BA1 1HA, UK
www.parragon.com/lovefood

ISBN: 978-1-4723-2552-5

Printed in China

Created and produced by Pene Parker and Becca Spry
Author and food stylist: Sara Lewis
Photographer: Haraala Hamilton

Notes for the reader
This book uses both metric and imperial measurements.
Follow the same units of measurement throughout: do not
mix metric and imperial. All spoon measurements are level:
teaspoons are assumed to be 5 ml and tablespoons are assumed
to be 15 ml. Unless otherwise stated, milk is assumed to be full
fat, individual vegetables are medium, and pepper is freshly
ground black pepper. The publisher recommends consulting a
doctor or other healthcare professional before embarking on
major dietary changes. The publisher disclaims any liability,
loss or risk that may be claimed or incurred as a consequence
— directly or indirectly — of the use and/or application of any
of the contents of this publication. While the author has made
every effort to ensure the information contained in this book is
accurate and up-to-date at the time of publication, medical and
pharmaceutical knowledge is constantly changing. Pregnant
and breastfeeding women are advised to avoid eating peanuts
and peanut products. Sufferers from nut allergies should
be aware that some of the ready-made ingredients used in
the recipes in this book may contain nuts. Always check the
packaging before use.

The author would like to thank John Lewis for the loan
of the Vitamix liquidizer.

6 The juice bar

80 Energy

12 Kick start

118 Health

46 Rehydrate

154 Detox

The juice bar

A juicer can help transform your health. With sugary cakes, high-salt and high-fat crisps, and ready meals within easy reach, and the ever-growing number of fast-food outlets, it is not surprising that levels of obesity, diabetes, heart disease, food allergies, digestive problems, asthma and eczema are rising. Good health is priceless, so why do we fuel our bodies with such junk and wonder at the results? The secret of good health is to take small steps towards long-term healthy eating. Introducing a delicious juice or smoothie daily can help boost your energy, vitamin and mineral levels and in turn improve the health of your skin, hair, eyes and fingernails, as well as your mood and feeling of well-being.

Health benefits

Health professionals recommend that we eat five 80 g/2¾ oz or more portions of fruit and vegetables per day (about one-third of our total daily food consumption). Yet the average consumption is nearer three portions, with only around 15 per cent of people meeting the target. Studies show that people who eat plenty of fruit and vegetables have a lower risk of developing high blood pressure, heart disease, strokes, obesity and some cancers.

It is estimated that diet is likely to contribute to the development of one-third of cancers. Eating more fruit and vegetables is the second most important cancer-prevention strategy after stopping smoking. Other health benefits include the delay in degenerative eye conditions, improved bone and digestive health and reduced symptoms of asthma.

As juices are made using raw ingredients, their nutritional content is high. Many vitamins and minerals are water-soluble, so are lost when cooked in water, and lots are destroyed by heat. When juiced, fruit and vegetables rehydrate the body and provide nutrients in a form that is easy to digest.

Fresh juices and smoothies energize you and can boost your sporting prowess. Smoothies, made in a blender with the whole, prepared fruit whizzed together, release energy into the body slowly, so can help us avoid the peaks and troughs that may lead to mood swings.

Weight-loss programme

Juices can play a key part in a weight-loss programme. You can kick-start a diet by replacing two meals each day with a juice for just two days. After that, replace one meal each day with a juice. Alternatively, if you usually have a mid-morning high-fat or high-sugar snack, or an evening glass of wine, choose a lower-calorie juice instead.

Juices for the family

We can all benefit from juice, from small kids bringing home colds and viruses, to youngsters battling hormones, exam stress and spots, to stressed-out parents, to grandparents and anyone recovering from illness. When giving juices to kids, if you don't let on what's in each drink you'll be amazed at how many veggies you can sneak into them! Curly kale and broccoli are mild, especially when mixed with naturally sweet apple, pineapple, beetroot or parsnip. The key is to get a good mix of flavours. There are three main ways of making a juice: in an electric juicer, a blender or by using a citrus press.

Electric juicers

Electric juicers have come a long way since the 1980s. You get what you pay for, so shop around and do your homework. If the price sounds too good to be true, then the machine may not have the muscle to do the job properly. Here are the things to consider when buying one.

What kind of juices do you want to make?
If you want to juice a mixture of fruit and vegetables, from root vegetables to broccoli to green leafy vegetables, go for a mid-priced centrifugal juicer. These tall models look a bit like a food processor and have a metal basket with teeth that spin round as you press foods through the chute. The juice is collected in a jug and the debris in a pulp container.

If you want to juice your own wheatgrass and lots of green leafy vegetables, then a masticating juicer is for you. These look a little like a mincing machine and work by crushing fruit and vegetables against a stainless-steel filter with a slowly rotating screw. They take longer to use, are fiddly to clean and the good ones tend to be pricey.

Blenders

Blenders vary greatly in motor power, speed settings, jug capacity and price. Some of the more powerful models can crush ice, but not all, so check with your manual before doing this. Their efficiency will greatly affect the texture of your juice, and as many kids and adults hate bits, it might be worth upgrading to a better model if your machine lacks muscle.

For less powerful machines, chop fruit up small, especially pineapples and grapefruits, before blending. Put just a few pieces in the blender to begin with, then add the rest through the gap in the lid while the motor is running. Crush ice before adding, or stir cubes into a finished drink.

Smaller 'personal' blenders with detachable drinking containers can be perfect for making a quick drink. Unscrew the blades and screw on the lid; you don't even need to decant the juice into a separate glass before drinking.

If using a blender, you will need to add liquid in the form of chilled water; rice, almond or soya milk; yogurt or juice. Food processors may be used in the same way, but they can have a bigger bowl so are not always great for single servings.

How big is the chute? If you have a big chute, ingredients such as apples, pears and beetroots can be added whole.

How many speeds are there? Two speeds are great: choose low for fleshy fruits and vegetables such as tomatoes, and high for hard fruits and vegetables such as apples.

What about the pulp container? Choose one that is a good size so that you don't have to empty it after you have made just one drink.

Is the machine easy to put together? If it's too fiddly then you won't use it.

Can the machine go in the dishwasher? Okay, so the detachable parts are bulky, and no one is suggesting that the motorized base goes in the dishwasher, but if you are rushing out to work in the morning and want to have a healthy juice, this could save you vital minutes.

Hand-held electric wands

These can be used for making blended juices. They are not suitable for blending hard ingredients such as apples and root vegetables, but can work well if you press these ingredients through a juicer first and then whizz the juice up with softer fruits such as berries and grapes.

Citrus press

For the odd orange or lemon, a heavy glass, china or stainless-steel press with a ridged domed top will work fine. Choose one with a pip collector and large moat or attached container to collect the juice. Keen cooks often like a small wooden reamer, but you will also need a little bowl to catch the juice. Also available are chrome-plated free-standing extractors with a hinged arm that presses the fruit down onto the squeezer as the juice feeds down into a chrome cup below. Some food processors come with a citrus juicer attachment, but if you plan to make more than one glass of juice at a time, it might be worth buying a separate electric citrus juicer.

Extra bits of kit

Small vegetable brush or new nail brush to scrub fruit and veg that don't need peeling.

Chopping board, good veg knife and peeler.

Biodegradable food bags; add one to the pulp container when juicing.

Ice-cube trays (unless you have a fridge that makes ice cubes and crushed ice). They are also great for freezing juice.

Choosing fruit & vegetables

As a rule of thumb, if the fruits or vegetables don't look good enough to eat then they are not good enough to juice or blend. It can be tempting to use up that elderly banana or slightly battered pear in a juice, but resist the urge.

Glam up your glass

Citrus twists – cut a thin slice from an orange, lemon or lime, then cut a slit into the centre. Twist the slice and perch it on the glass.

Corkscrews – pare a long, thin strip of zest from an orange, lemon or lime. Wrap it tightly around a skewer, hold for a minute, then slide it off and drape the corkscrew over the glass.

Thin slices of courgette or carrot can be pared from the length of the vegetable using a swivel-bladed peeler. Insert a skewer in two places for a curved boat-shape or roll it up tightly.

Foodie stirrers – try cinnamon sticks, halved lemon grass stems or celery sticks.

Mini-skewers – thread a few pieces of fruit onto a cocktail stick, then rest it on the glass.

Salt or sugar kick – dip the top of the glass in lemon juice, then in salt or caster sugar.

How to use a juicer

Simply prepare fruit and vegetables and press them through the juicer. What could be easier? There's no need to add water, but you can if you wish; it depends on the weather, how thirsty you are and how strong-tasting the juice is.

Wheatgrass

Wheatgrass is difficult to juice unless you have a masticating juicer. It's potent too, so don't try to drink too much in one go. If you juice it on its own, aim to serve just 3-tablespoon shots. Alternatively, stir 1 teaspoon of powdered wheatgrass into your juice; it may not contain quite as much nutrition, but it is easy to use.

Root vegetables

Sweet potatoes, beetroots, carrots and parsnips just need a trim and a good scrub. There's no need to peel fresh ginger; just add skin and all. Depending on the width of your juicer chute, you may not even need to cut root veg into pieces.

Melons

Remove the skin from melons. There's no need to remove the seeds as the juicer can make super-speedy work of separating these.

Citrus fruits

Pare away the zest, leaving some of the pith on as it contains valuable nutrients. (You can leave some of the zest on lemons and limes for a tangy citrus hit if you prefer, but not on oranges or grapefruits.) If you want a thinner drink, squeeze the juice from the fruit before adding it.

Pineapples & kiwi fruits

Remove the skin from pineapples, but there's no need to remove the eyes or core. You can leave the skin on kiwi fruits, but the juice will not look as vibrant if you do.

Best for blending

The blender is best for softer fruits and vegetables. Avocados, tomatoes, bananas, soft juicy berries and seedless grapes all work brilliantly and blitz to a wonderfully smooth drink in a blender. But you will need to add yogurt, or unsweetened soya, almond or rice milk, or a splash of chilled water to help the blades whizz round.

Prepare fruits and vegetables exactly as you would for a salad: remove stones; peel off dark green, furry or knobbly skins; and peel the zest from citrus fruits but leave on some of the pith for extra fibre and a creamy texture. You don't need to skin tomatoes. Peel harder fruits such as pineapples and chop them into small pieces (there is no need to remove the core of a pineapple). Root vegetables, red cabbages, apples and pears are too hard for blending, so must be fed through a juicer before being added to a blender and mixed with softer fruits and vegetables. Seeds and grains are best ground to a fine powder in a blender before you add them to a juice.

Softer vegetables & herbs

Soft vegetables, including lettuce, broccoli florets, cabbage, celery, courgettes, cucumber, kale, tomatoes and peppers, and herbs should be added to the chute between solid vegetables or fruit where possible.

Papayas

Cut papayas in half and scoop out the seeds, then thinly cut the flesh away from the peel. They don't produce much juice.

Apples & pears

Wash apples and pears well, then juice them whole or cut them in half if needed to fit them into the juicer chute.

Mangos

Cut a thick slice off the top and bottom of a mango to reveal the large, flat stone. Cut around this stone, pull away the flesh and cut it from the skin. The fruit doesn't produce much juice, so mix it with melon, apple or pineapple.

Kick start

Berry breakfast

This breakfast-in-a-glass is packed with sustaining nutrients to keep up your energy levels all morning.

Serves 1

* 200 g/7 oz strawberries
* 100 g/3½ oz raspberries
* 100 ml/3½ fl oz unsweetened rice, almond or soya milk
* 40 g/1½ oz unsweetened muesli

To make this juice

Cut a strawberry in half and reserve one half. Remove the hulls from the remaining strawberries. Put the strawberries and raspberries in a blender and whizz to a purée. Add the milk and muesli and whizz until almost smooth. Pour into a glass, top with the reserved strawberry half and serve.

Sensational strawberries

Strawberries have more vitamin C than any other red berries and so have great antiviral and antibacterial properties. They are rich in beta carotene, which is converted by the body into vitamin A. Their natural fruit sugars also give the body an early-morning energy boost. Strawberries contain lignin, which may help reduce blood cholesterol.

Say yes to soya!

Adding soya yogurt or soya milk to a juice is a great way to boost its protein levels. Many soya milks are fortified with vitamin D and calcium, which means they can also help strengthen bones and teeth. Choose soya yogurt or milk that is unsweetened. They are free from the milk sugar lactose, too.

Nutrient boosters

Fruit and vegetables
are packed with nutrients
– but add a few seeds,
grains or nuts to your juice or
smoothie and it will be
an energy-lifting
protein fix or vitamin
and mineral
power-boost.

Nuts

Bursting with protein, just a
tablespoon of nuts can give a boost to
any fresh juice. Grind them in a blender,
then add fruits and whizz them up or
store them in a jar in the fridge ready to
stir into a juice. They are high in fat, which
bumps up the calories, but they contain
essential fatty acids, are rich in vitamin
E, and include most of the B group
of vitamins and a whole lot of
minerals.

Wheat germ

Wheat germ is the small part inside
a wheat grain, from which a plant
grows. It should not be confused with
wheat bran, which is the outer, fibrous part
of the grain. It is packed with protein to aid
muscle development, vitamin E to boost
immunity and aid skin health, omega-3
fatty acids, zinc, magnesium, some
of the B group of vitamins and
fibre. It is sold as flakes.

Oats

A great source
of energy, oats'
complex carbohydrates
mean that they are
digested slowly and so
help maintain sugar levels
in the blood. Rich in soluble
fibre, they help lower blood
cholesterol levels too. They are
low in fat and a good source
of protein. Grind in a blender,
then whizz with fruit and
vegetables or stir into fresh
juices. They contain avenin,
a protein similar to gluten,
which some
gluten-intolerant
people are also
intolerant to.

Sesame, sunflower & pumpkin seeds

Each of these seeds contains protein, B vitamins, vitamin E and fibre. One tablespoon can contain as many as 100 calories, depending on which seed you choose, so they add an energy boost to drinks. They contain monounsaturated fats (good fats) too!

Ancient Aztecs believed that just 1 tablespoon of chia seeds could sustain a warrior for 24 hours.

Chia seeds

The new seeds on the block, chia deserve a special mention. Just 2 tablespoons can add valuable protein, fibre and omega-3 and omega-6 fatty acids to a drink, not to mention calcium, iron, copper and zinc. They're almost flavourless, so go unnoticed when ground and mixed into a juice. When combined with liquid, they form a gel, so help you feel full for longer.

Flaxseeds & hemp seeds

Sometimes called linseeds, golden or dark flaxseeds are rich in B vitamins, magnesium, manganese, and omega-3 and omega-6 fatty acids. They are also high in fibre and phytochemicals, including antioxidants (although these are not found in the oil). Hemp seeds are the only seeds that contains all essential amino acids, so are a great source of protein.

Power-boosting beets

This robust, vibrant-coloured juice is packed with big flavours and energy-boosting nutrients to get you going in the morning.

Serves 1

* 2 beetroots, halved
* 2 large carrots, halved
* 2 celery sticks, halved
* 5-cm/2-inch piece of cucumber
* 2 red-skinned apples, halved
* 30 g/1 oz walnut pieces, finely ground
* small handful of ice (optional)

Whizz it up

Cut two wafer-thin slices off one of the beetroot halves and reserve. Feed the beetroot and carrots, then celery and cucumber, then apples through a juicer. Stir in the walnuts. Half-fill a glass with ice (if using), then pour in the juice. Thread the beetroot slices through a cocktail stick, lay this on top of the glass and serve immediately.

Sweet beetroot

Beetroot has one of the highest sugar levels of any vegetable, with the equivalent of 1 teaspoon of natural fruit sugar in each 115 g/4 oz portion, so it gives a great energy boost. It also contains folates, vitamin C and potassium, which help to regulate blood pressure and nerve function.

Beat the morning blues

Full of vitamin C-packed berries, this hearty juice is a truly supercharged breakfast immunity boost!

Serves 1

* 1 pear, halved
* 150 g/5½ oz blueberries
* 100 ml/3½ fl oz soya yogurt
* ½ tsp agave syrup
* 2 tsp flaked almonds, toasted

Give it a whirl

Feed the pear through a juicer. Pour the juice into a blender, add the blueberries and whizz. Add the yogurt and agave syrup and whizz again until smooth. Pour into a glass, sprinkle with the almonds and serve.

Agave syrup

The succulent agave plant, which is related to the yucca and lily, grows in the southern and western United States and in tropical South America. Agave syrup, extracted from agave plants, is sold in health-food shops and is used as a sweetener. It is considered by many to be superior to sugar because, when compared with other sweeteners, it has a low-glycaemic index, which means that it won't cause a sharp rise or fall in blood sugar when eaten.

Health notes

Our bodies need protein, which is found in almonds and soya yogurt, for the growth and repair of everything from muscles and bones to hair and fingernails. There's calcium and vitamin D in some fortified brands of soya yogurt too. This breakfast-boosting drink also provides the minerals phosphorus, magnesium and zinc, which are great for our bones and teeth.

Berry kick-start

This energizing, gorgeous-looking smoothie is a delicious and healthy way to kick-start your day.

Serves 1

* 175 g/6 oz blueberries
* 115 g/4 oz cranberries
* 150 ml/5 fl oz natural yogurt
* 2 tsp clear honey
* 4 tbsp chilled water

To make this juice

Put the blueberries and cranberries in a blender and whizz until smooth. Add the yogurt, honey and water and whizz again. Pour into a glass and serve.

Don't fancy honey & sugar? Try these...

Honey supplies energy in the form of simple carbohydrates and is a mixture of fructose and glucose. The clearer the honey, the higher the fructose level. Sweet foods stimulate the brain to produce endorphins, the body's natural pain killers. Agave syrup, brown rice syrup and date syrup can all be used instead of honey. Agave syrup is naturally sweeter than honey. Brown rice syrup has a mild caramel flavour and is like maple syrup. Date syrup is a thick, concentrated purée of lightly cooked dates; you can make it by gently simmering dates with a little water, cinnamon and vanilla, then puréeing and storing in the fridge.

Superfood: blueberries

Blueberries are packed with more antioxidants than many other fruits and vegetables. These antioxidants, called flavonoids, help to mop up damaging free radicals and help to protect the body from premature ageing, heart disease, cancer and degenerative diseases. Forty blueberries (80 g/2¾ oz) contain seven and a half times more antioxidant activity than a small banana. They also contain vitamin C, which our body needs daily, natural fruit sugar for energy, and pectin, thought to help lower cholesterol and act as an anti-inflammatory.

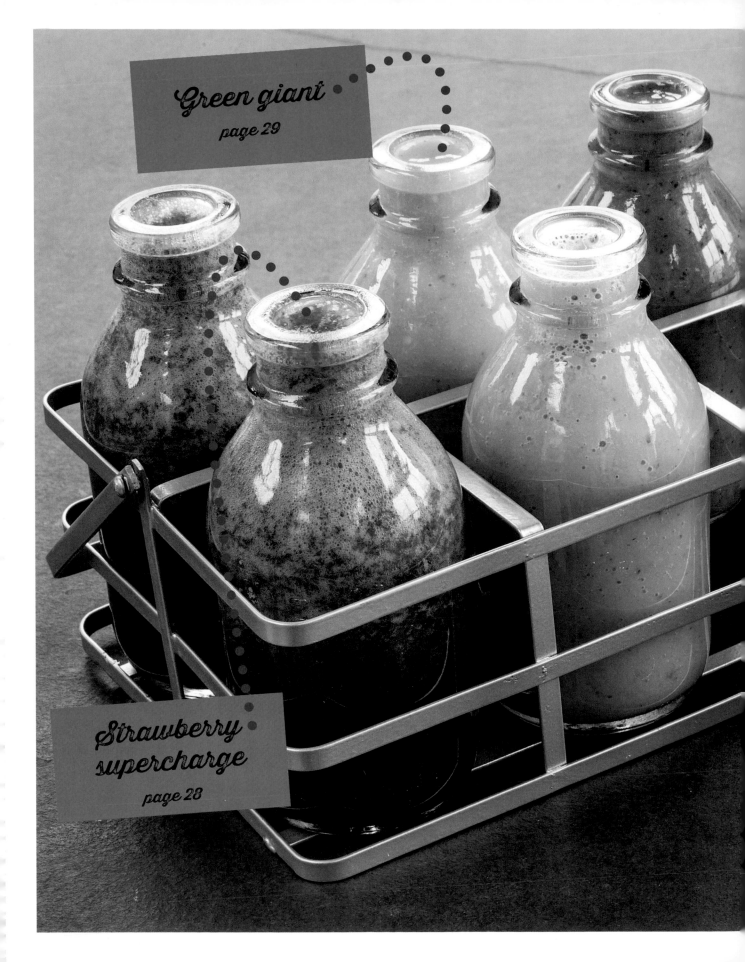

Green giant

page 29

Strawberry
supercharge

page 28

Ready, steady, go!

Breakfast is arguably the most important meal of the day, and this shake includes lots of vital nutrients. It's quick to make, tasty and filling, but won't leave you feeling heavy.

Serves 1

* 20 g/¾ oz pumpkin seeds
* 20 g/¾ oz flaxseeds (linseeds)
* 20 g/¾ oz oz flaked almonds
* 115 g/4 oz raspberries
* 115 g/4 oz blueberries
* 225 g/8 oz vanilla soya yogurt
* 125 ml/4 fl oz chilled water

Mix it up

Put the pumpkin seeds, flaxseeds and almonds in a blender and whizz until finely ground. Add the raspberries, blueberries, yogurt and water and whizz until smooth. Pour into a glass and serve.

Quick banana boosters

Need to grab a quick breakfast? Then try these fab banana-based energy drinks. They're super-quick, super-simple and super-healthy!

1

Banana & blueberry

* 1 banana, peeled and roughly chopped
* 115 g/4 oz blueberries
* 125 ml/4 fl oz unsweetened rice milk
* small handful of crushed ice

2

Banana & kiwi

* 1 banana, peeled and roughly chopped
* 2 kiwi fruit, peeled and roughly chopped
* 125 ml/4 fl oz unsweetened rice milk
* small handful of crushed ice

3

Banana & mango

* 1 banana, peeled and roughly chopped
* ½ mango, pitted, peeled and flesh roughly chopped
* 125 ml/4 fl oz unsweetened rice milk
* small handful of crushed ice

Serves 1

For each drink, put all the ingredients in a blender and whizz until smooth. Pour into a glass and serve immediately.

Happiness is... a banana!

Feeling a bit down? Forget about chocolate, munch on a banana instead! It is the only fruit to contain the amino acid tryptophan plus vitamin B6, which together help the body produce serotonin (the natural chemical that helps to lift your mood). Naturally rich in fruit sugar and starch, bananas are great energy-boosting foods and have a high amount of potassium. They can help to regulate blood pressure, lower the risk of heart attacks and strokes and reduce the risk of cancer.

Blackberry blaster

Banish those morning blues with this cinnamon-spiced, dairy-free juice. It's bursting with vitamins and minerals, and will keep you energized until lunchtime.

Serves 1

* 3 large red-skinned plums, halved and pitted
* 40 g/1½ oz red curly kale
* 1 pear, halved
* 115 g/4 oz blackberries
* 20 g/¾ oz wheat germ
* pinch of ground cinnamon (optional)
* small handful of crushed ice
* 4–6 tbsp chilled water

Time to get started

Feed the plums, then kale, then pear through a juicer. Pour the juice into a blender. Add the blackberries (reserving one to decorate), wheat germ, cinnamon (if using) and crushed ice, and whizz until smooth. Add the water to taste and whizz again, until smooth. Pour into a glass. Thread a blackberry through a cocktail stick, add it to the glass, and serve immediately.

Blackberries: nature's aspirin

Energy-boosting blackberries are a good source of vitamin C, folates and fibre. More unusually, they also contain salicylates, a natural aspirin-like compound, so if you are allergic to aspirin steer clear of this fruit.

Vegetable tummy treat

Wake up your body and stimulate your digestive system with this fresh-tasting orange and-tomato drink. There is also a kick in the tail delivered by the chilli, to shake up those taste buds!

Serves 1

* 3 oranges, zest and a little pith removed
* 1 carrot, halved
* 2 tomatoes, roughly chopped
* 125 ml/4 fl oz chilled water
* 1 small green chilli, halved
* 2 celery sticks, thickly sliced
* 2 tsp hemp seed oil

Give it a whirl

Cut 2 oranges in half and feed them and the carrot through a juicer. Pour the juice into a blender. Roughly chop and deseed the remaining orange, then put it, the tomatoes and water in the blender and whizz until smooth. Add the chilli and celery and whizz again until blended. Pour into a glass, stir in the hemp seed oil and serve.

Hurray for hemp seed oil

Hemp seed oil contains a good balance of both omega-3 and omega-6 fats. The Department of Health finds that it is the balance of these fats that is most important in maintaining health and protecting us from disease.

Peachy
wake-up call
page 39

Carrot & ginger
vitamin vitality
page 38

Tropical sunrise & shine

Cheer up the dullest morning with this tropical fruit blend, and ramp up its nutrition with a sprinkling of chia seeds. If you're in a hurry, pack the juice into an insulated flask and enjoy it instead of a caffeine-loaded tea or coffee when you get to work.

Serves 1

* 20 g/¾ oz goji berries
* 15 g/½ oz chia seeds
* ½ papaya, peeled, deseeded and roughly chopped
* ¼ pineapple, peeled and roughly chopped
* ½ lime, zest and a little pith removed, deseeded and roughly chopped
* 225 ml/8 fl oz chilled water
* small handful of crushed ice (optional)

Bring me sunshine!

Put the goji berries and chia seeds in a blender and whizz until finely ground. Add the papaya, pineapple, lime and water and whizz until smooth. Add the crushed ice (if using) and whizz again, until blended. Pour into a glass and serve immediately.

Rehydrate

Go, kids, go!

Start giving your kids the healthy-eating message when they are young with these juices. The oranges are squeezed to make the juices extra smooth.

1

Strawberry & banana

* 150 g/5½ oz strawberries, hulled
* 1 banana, peeled and roughly chopped
* ½ orange, juice squeezed
* small handful of crushed ice
* chilled water, to taste

Serves 1

For each drink, put all the fruit and juice in a blender and whizz until smooth. Add the crushed ice and whizz again. Pour into a glass, top up with water to taste, and serve immediately.

Kids' nutrition

Kids need nutrient-dense foods to maintain energy levels and good fats from dairy foods for fat-soluble vitamins that are vital for growing bones and teeth. They need fibre too, but not too much of it or those tiny tummies will fill up before enough protein, vitamins and minerals have been consumed.

2

Avocado & grape

* ½ avocado, pitted and flesh scooped from the skin
* 115 g/4 oz green seedless grapes
* ½ orange, juice squeezed
* small handful of crushed ice
* chilled water, to taste

Choosing a blender

Most kids hate bits, so buy the best blender you can afford. Budget ones don't always make smooth drinks!

Juice benefits

Fruit and vegetable juices are great ways to sneak lots of nutrients into your child's diet without him or her noticing. Serve with a sandwich for a healthy lunch.

3

Carrot & papaya

* ½ papaya, peeled, deseeded and roughly chopped
* ½ orange, juice squeezed
* 2 carrots, halved and fed through a juicer
* small handful of crushed ice
* chilled water, to taste

Ruby fruit reviver

There's nothing more refreshing than a locally grown strawberry in the summer, but this smoothie can be enjoyed at any time of year – just shop carefully for the imported strawberries that really smell and taste as they should: biggest doesn't necessarily mean best!

Serves 1

* 1 ruby red grapefruit, zest and a little pith removed, deseeded and roughly chopped
* ¼ cucumber, roughly chopped
* 150 g/5½ oz strawberries, hulled
* small handful of crushed ice (optional)

Great ruby grapefruits

Ruby grapefruits contain lycopene, an antioxidant thought to help protect the body against some cancers and lower the risk of heart disease. They're sweeter than white-fleshed varieties and packed with vitamin C. In this drink, the strawberries also contain antioxidants and vitamin C, plus ellagic acid (which may help protect against collagen destruction and the inflammatory response after sun damage that can cause wrinkles).

Time for a revival

Put the grapefruit and cucumber in a blender and whizz until smooth. Add the strawberries and crushed ice (if using) and whizz until blended. Pour into a glass and serve immediately.

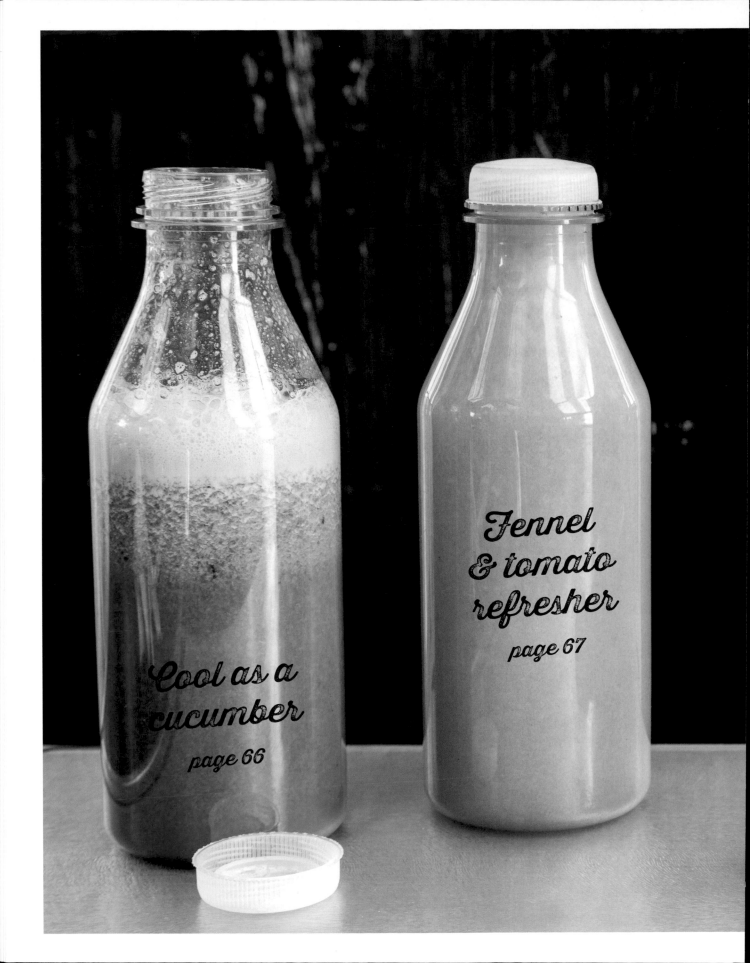

Cool as a
cucumber

page 66

Fennel
& tomato
refresher

page 67

Peach perfect rehydrator

Think of peach melba blended into a foaming fruity drink; perfect on a balmy summer's afternoon. Why not pack this juice into an insulated flask and enjoy it as part of a family picnic or quick lunch for one on a park bench?

Serves 1

* 20 g/¾ oz goji berries
* 2 peaches, halved, pitted and roughly chopped
* 150 g/5½ oz raspberries
* 225 ml/8 fl oz chilled water
* small handful of crushed ice

For a peach of a drink...

Put the goji berries in a blender and whizz until finely ground. Add all the remaining ingredients and whizz until smooth. Pour into a glass and serve immediately.

Peach
perfect
rehydrator

Energy

Energy-boosting facts

If you need a quick energy boost, make your juice rich in naturally sweet fruits, such as apples, oranges and berries. For a sustained boost, choose fruits and vegetables with less sugar and more starch, such as beetroots, bananas and avocados, plus ground grains and seeds.

Sugar overload

The pancreas secretes insulin, and this controls your body's uptake of glucose (blood sugar). If your diet is too high in sugar, you can upset the delicate balance of your blood-sugar level, causing fluctuations in energy and mood that can make you feel tired and irritable. The excess sugar is then stored in the liver as glycogen and as fat around the body.

Types of carbohydrates

Carbohydrates supply energy to the body. The digestive system converts them into glucose (blood sugar) and this is then carried in the blood and used for energy. Carbohydrates can be broken down into three groups: sugar, starches and fibre.

Sugar

Try to focus your sugar consumption on natural sugars found in fruits and vegetables rather than refined sugars found in biscuits, cakes, pastries, jams, soft drinks, sweets and some ready-prepared foods.

Starches

Good sources of starch include bananas, parsnips, sweet potatoes, carrots, beetroots, sweetcorn and wholegrain cereals. Refined starches (the baddies) are found in biscuits, pastries, cakes, sugary breakfast cereals, white bread, pasta and rice, among other foods.

Fibre

Fibre is found in fruits and vegetables, cereals (especially wholegrains), pulses, nuts and seeds.

Juices after exercise

If we have too little energy we may tire quickly, lose concentration and have delayed recovery. Therefore, after exercise, it is important to boost our energy levels, and a freshly made juice is a good way to do this. The most effective refuelling occurs within 30 minutes of exercise.

What is an isotonic drink?

An isotonic drink is a sports drink used to replace fluids and electrolytes and has a similar concentration to the body's own fluids. Generally made up of glucose and water, isotonic drinks contain added vitamins and salts to compensate for those lost during sweating. Typically, they contain between four and eight per cent carbohydrates, to improve stamina. They are usually commercially made, but can be home-made with an equal mix of fresh fruit or vegetable juice and water, and a pinch of salt.

Hypertonic drinks contain between 10 and 15 per cent carbohydrates and rarely contain electrolytes. The higher the level of carbohydrates in a drink, the greater the energy boost and the slower the stomach will empty, reducing urine output and encouraging fluid retention. They should only be consumed during and after endurance events such as a marathon run, but make sure you follow up with water to rehydrate later. Choose fruit smoothies or drinks made with whole fruits or vegetables such as bananas, avocados or beetroots, and soya yogurt or milk.

Hypotonic drinks are intended to quickly replace water lost during sweating. They do not generally contain carbohydrates, but they do contain sodium and potassium, which tend to be lost when we sweat.

Water to aid concentration

Ever sat at your desk and struggled to concentrate? Then it might not just be an energy boost you need. Water and natural fruit juices are also essential. Your brain is made up of 75 per cent water, so keeping hydrated is vital. When you are dehydrated, your concentration can decrease by 13 per cent and your short-term memory by seven per cent, so keep your fluid levels up – especially when revising for an exam. We also need water to help maintain normal blood pressure and body temperature. It is important to drink plenty of fluids, even when you don't feel thirsty, especially in hot weather or after exercise. Aim for a mix of fresh juices or water rather than caffeine-loaded tea or coffee, which can dehydrate, or sugary commercial drinks.

Blueberry blast

The blueberry is a superhero in the food world. When mixed with pear, natural yogurt and thirst-quenching chilled water, as in this drink, it will get you through the most hectic of schedules. You can use two apples instead of the water if you prefer; just juice them with the pear.

Serves 1

* 1 pear, halved
* 115 g/4 oz blueberries
* 175 ml/6 fl oz cup natural yogurt
* 20 g/¾ oz wheat germ
* 175 ml/6 fl oz chilled water
* small handful of crushed ice (optional)

How to make it

Feed the pear through a juicer. Pour the juice into a blender, add the blueberries, yogurt, wheat germ and water and whizz. Add the crushed ice (if using) and whizz again, until smooth. Pour into a glass and serve immediately.

Blueberries: good mood food

The antioxidant power of blueberries has been shown to help stabilize brain function and protect the neural tissue from oxidative stress – which may improve memory and learning and reduce symptoms of depression.

Keep it for later...
If you don't drink this all at once
the wheat germ tends to swell, so you
might need to add an extra splash of
water when you finish it later.

Single shot sports boosters

Have one of these potent juices just before you start strenuous exercise for a vitamin and mineral boost to energize muscles and aid performance. Transport them to the gym in a well-sealed insulated sports flask.

Serves 1

Beetroot booster
* 2 beetroots, halved
* 4 tbsp chilled water (optional)

Kiwi fruit booster
* 2 kiwi fruits

Blueberry booster
* 150 g/5½ oz blueberries
* 4 tbsp chilled water

To make these juices

* For the Beetroot booster, feed the beetroot through a juicer. Pour into a glass, top up with the water (if using) and serve.

* For the Kiwi fruit booster, feed the kiwi fruits through a juicer. Pour into a glass and serve.

* For the Blueberry booster, put the blueberries and water in a blender, then whizz until smooth. Pour into a glass and serve.

Water versus juices

When you exercise you lose many of the minerals in your body through sweat. Water alone will rehydrate you, but so can juices. Home-made fruit and vegetable juices also boost your energy and vitamin and mineral intake and help you rehydrate more quickly, speeding up recovery time. But best of all is to drink a mixture of the two in a home-made isotonic sports drink.

Raspberry rejuvenator

Raspberries and bananas give the body a slowly released energy boost to re-energize you in a sustained way.

Serves 1

* 30 g/1 oz goji berries
* 1 small banana, peeled and roughly chopped
* 115 g/4 oz raspberries
* 2 oranges, juice squeezed
* small handful of crushed ice (optional)
* chilled water, to taste

Whizz it up

Put the goji berries in a blender and whizz until finely ground. Add the banana, raspberries and orange juice and whizz again. Add the crushed ice (if using) and whizz again, until smooth. Add water to taste, pour into a glass and serve immediately.

Balancing your carbs & protein

For sportsmen and sportswomen it's particularly important to get the right mix of protein and carbohydrates. Too few carbs and your low energy levels will make it difficult for you to train and perform at your best, and your body will use any protein in your food and drink for energy rather than for building muscles.

Juicing oranges

Oranges vary hugely in the amount of juice that they produce. If they are kept at room temperature they will be easier to squeeze. Adjust this juice with water as needed.

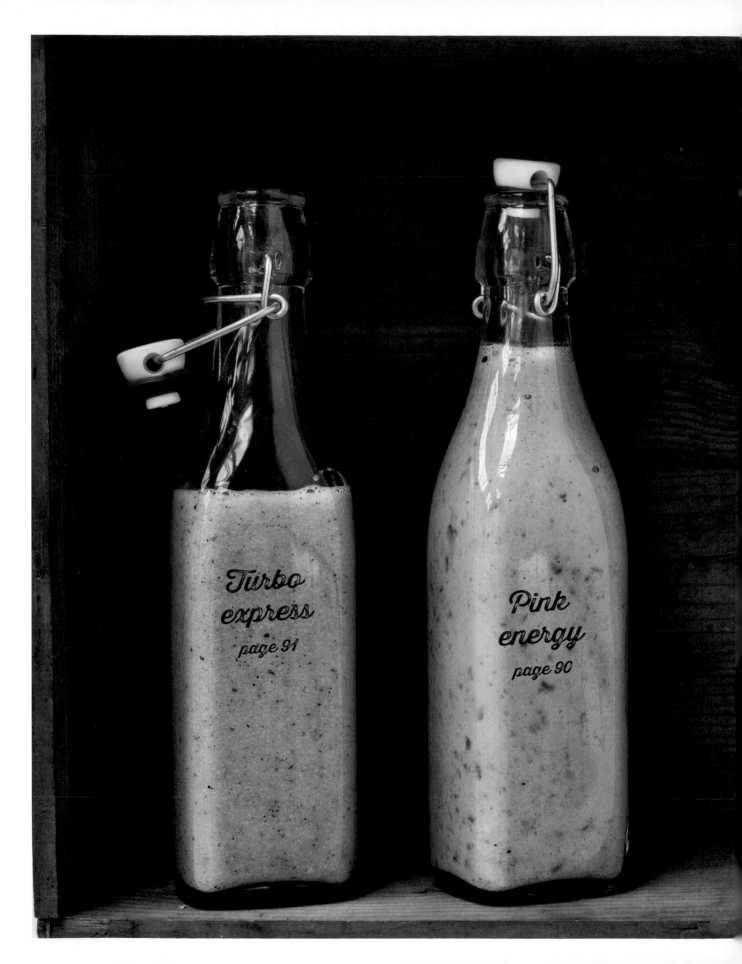

Peach energizer

The grapefruit blast in this drink will perk you up and sharpen your senses, while the peach will provide natural sugars to boost your energy levels and the ginger will soothe and comfort. It's so much better for you than a cup of tea and a chocolate biscuit!

Serves 1

* 1 pink or ruby grapefruit, zest and a little pith removed, halved
* 1 carrot, halved
* 1-cm/½-inch piece of fresh ginger
* 1 large peach, pitted and roughly chopped
* 1 tbsp light tahini
* 125 ml/4 fl oz chilled water (optional)
* small handful of crushed ice

Make it peachy

Feed the grapefruit and then carrot and ginger through a juicer. Pour the juice into a blender, add the peach, tahini, water (if using) and crushed ice and whizz until smooth. Pour into a glass and serve immediately.

Peach energizer

Muscular magic

page 102

Natural apple
booster

page 103

Tropical refresher

Papaya and mango are both rich in natural fruit sugars, which give an energy boost. They're easy to digest and gentle on the stomach.

Serves 1

* 1 banana, peeled and roughly chopped
* ½ papaya, peeled, deseeded and roughly chopped
* ½ mango, pitted, peeled and roughly chopped
* 1 lime, juice squeezed
* 2-cm/¾-inch piece of fresh ginger, peeled and finely grated
* 2 tsp hemp oil
* 125 ml/4 fl oz unsweetened rice, almond or soya milk
* small handful of crushed ice

For a tropical island dream...

Put the banana, papaya and mango in a blender and whizz until smooth. Add the lime, ginger, hemp oil, milk and crushed ice and whizz again. Pour into a glass and serve immediately.

Superfood: kale

From shiny blue-green to red, this ruffled, leafy
vegetable boasts a healthy amount of calcium,
vitamin B, vitamin C and beta carotene. The
antioxidant lutein helps to protect us from
macular eye degeneration, while indoles offer
protection against oestrogen-related cancers
and sulforaphane may help boost the liver's
ability to detoxify carcinogenic compounds.
Back in 1939, the government encouraged
everyone to grow kale in the 'Dig for Victory'
campaign as it is easy for even a novice
gardener to grow and highly nutritious.

Mango & lime bone-builder

This pretty, green-speckled drink looks mango-free, but the fruit's natural sweetness balances the kale, and its flavour comes through even if its colour is disguised.

Serves 1

* 1 tbsp sesame seeds
* ½ lime, juice squeezed
* 30 g/1 oz green curly kale, torn into pieces
* 1 mango, pitted, peeled and roughly chopped
* 225 ml/8 fl oz unsweetened rice, almond or soya milk
* small handful of crushed ice

Good for your bones

Calcium-boosting sesame seeds, kale and fortified soya milk all help to maintain bone strength and function of the nerves and muscles. The addition of vitamin D to the soya milk aids absorption.

Give it a whirl

Put the sesame seeds in a blender and whizz until finely ground. Add the lime juice, kale and mango and whizz until blended. Add the milk and crushed ice and whizz again, until smooth. Pour into a glass and serve immediately.

Grape & lychee reviver

Go oriental with fragrant lychees, thought by the Chinese to be the symbol of love. Blend them with creamy, smooth avocado and naturally sweet grapes for the perfect pick-me-up to rehydrate and fight fatigue.

Serves 1

* 300 g/10½ oz green grapes
* 55 g/2 oz young spinach
* ½ ripe avocado, pitted and flesh scooped from the skin, plus a slice to serve (optional)
* 5 lychees, peeled and pitted
* small handful of crushed ice
* 125 ml/4 fl oz chilled water

Whizz it up

Feed the grapes and spinach through a juicer. Pour the juice into a blender, add the avocado, lychees and crushed ice and whizz until smooth. Add the water and whizz again. Pour into a glass, add the avocado slice (if using) and serve immediately.

Grape nutrition

Grapes are a good source of potassium, although weight for weight they provide only one-twentieth of the vitamin C of kiwi fruits. The Greeks regarded them as an aphrodisiac, as they are the fruit of Dionysus, the Greek god of fertility and procreation.

Super-powered mango

You don't need to be a sportsman or sportswoman to benefit from an energy boost; coping with a young family can be just as tiring! Rather than reach for a chocolate biscuit or slice of cake to pick you up in the middle of the afternoon, try this energizing fruit blend of clementines, mango and apples. If clementines are out of season, you can use an orange.

Serves 1

* 2 clementines, zest and a little pith removed
* 1 mango, pitted and peeled
* 2 apples, halved
* small handful of ice, to serve (optional)
* chilled water, to taste
* 1 tsp clear honey

How to make this juice

Feed the clementines, mango and apples through a juicer. Half-fill a glass with ice (if using). Pour in the juice, top up with water to taste, stir in the honey and serve immediately.

How to prepare mango

Cut a thick slice off the top of the mango using a sharp knife, then cut one off the bottom to reveal a large, flattish oval stone. Cut around the stone, keeping all the trimmings. Push out the skin, cut the flesh into cubes, then cut the cubes off the skin.

Mango for energy

A mango is 14 per cent natural
sugar, and this can be quickly converted
into energy by the body. It is also rich in
beta carotene and vitamin C.

Body balancer

Look quickly at this drink and you could mistake it for a coffee swirled with hot milk, but it is actually dairy-free and caffeine-free. The prunes make it a natural laxative.

Serves 1

* 1 tbsp flaxseeds (linseeds)
* 85 g/3 oz ready-to-eat pitted prunes
* 1 small banana, peeled and roughly chopped
* 1 tbsp wheat germ
* 2 large oranges, juice squeezed
* 115 ml/4 fl oz vanilla soya yogurt
* 225 ml/8 fl oz chilled water

Whizz it up

Put the flaxseeds in a blender and whizz until finely ground. Add the prunes, banana and wheat germ and whizz again. Add the orange juice and half the yogurt and whizz again, until smooth. Add the water and whizz once more. Pour into a glass, add the remaining yogurt and swirl together with a teaspoon, then serve.

A natural laxative

Prunes are one of the most effective laxatives. They are rich in potassium, which is needed for the healthy function of cells, nerves and muscles and to regulate blood pressure. The natural cultures in the yogurt in this drink help restore the balance of healthy bacteria in your gut.

Spring clean

page 144

Body balancer

page 145

Multi-mineral bonanza

With spinach, beetroot, oranges and carrots, this drink provides a bumper beta carotene and vitamin C hit.

Serves 1

* 2 beetroots, halved
* 40 g/1½ oz young spinach
* 2 carrots, halved
* 2 oranges, zest and a little pith removed, halved
* 1 tbsp sesame seeds, finely ground
* small handful of ice
* sparkling mineral water, chilled, to taste

Mix it up!

Feed the beetroot, spinach and carrots, then oranges through a juicer. Stir in the ground sesame seeds. Half-fill a glass with ice, then pour in the juice, top up with sparkling water to taste and serve immediately.

Red pepper reviver

This fiery juice is sure to wake you up if you're having
a mid-morning snooze!

Serves 1

* 2 carrots, halved, plus
  strips of shredded carrot
  to garnish
* 2 tomatoes, halved
* 1 large red pepper, halved
* 2 tsp lemon juice
* freshly ground black pepper

Ready, steady, go

Feed the carrots, then tomatoes and red
pepper through a juicer. Stir in the lemon
juice and plenty of black pepper. Pour into
a glass, garnish with the strips of shredded
carrot and serve.

Thumbs up for tomatoes

Tomatoes are rich in lycopene, a carotenoid
pigment that turns them red. It is thought
this may help prevent some forms of cancer.
They are also a good source of potassium,
with smaller amounts of vitamins C and E.
They contain 90 per cent water, so are great
for rehydration too.

Cutting calories

The more you get into juicing, the less
appealing that takeaway snack will be.
Just cutting down 100 or 200 calories
a day can have a big impact on your
weight over the course of a year.

Red pep-up

Full of disease-fighting, anti-ageing antioxidants, this drink provides lots of energy from its natural sweetness to help you get through the day.

Serves 1

* 2 fennel bulbs with leaves, halved
* 1 apple, halved
* 1 small red pepper, halved
* 1 carrot, halved

Give it a whirl

Remove a few leaves from the fennel and reserve. Feed the apple, then fennel and pepper, then carrot through a juicer. Pour into a glass, garnish with the fennel leaves and serve.

Winter pick-me-up

Banish the winter blues with this nutrient-packed juice that boosts vitamin, mineral and energy levels.

Serves 1

* 1 parsnip, halved
* 2 carrots, halved, plus 2 carrot sticks to garnish
* 1 garlic clove
* 2 apples, halved
* 2 tbsp porridge oats
* 1 tbsp wheat germ
* 2 tsp clear honey
* small handful of ice (optional)

Whizz it up

Feed the parsnip, carrots and garlic, then apples through a juicer. Put the oats and wheat germ in a blender and whizz until finely ground. Add the honey and parsnip juice mix and whizz again, until smooth. Half-fill a glass with ice (if using). Pour in the juice, add the carrot sticks and serve immediately.

How to use wheat germ

Wheat germ flakes swell in your drinks. This means that if you don't serve a juice or smoothie as soon as you have made it, you will need to add a splash of chilled water to return it to the right consistency.

Buying parsnips

Buy parsnips a few weeks after the first
frost if you can, as much of the starch is
converted to sugar in a frost, so making them
taste sweeter.

Detox

Beet aid detox

This thirst-quenching, nutrient-packed juice is bursting with vitamins and minerals. Since Roman times, beetroot has been thought of as an aphrodisiac, so who knows what might happen when you feel detoxed and re-energized?

Serves 1

* 1 beetroot, halved
* ½ lime
* 55 g/2 oz red chard
* 675 g/1 lb 8 oz watermelon, thickly sliced and peel removed
* small handful of ice (optional)

Smoothie steps

Feed the beetroot and lime, then chard and watermelon through a juicer. Half-fill a glass with ice (if using), then pour in the juice and serve immediately.

Health notes

Beetroot contains virtually all the vitamins and minerals needed to give your whole body a boost. Watermelon's high water content helps to rehydrate and plump up your skin.

Citrus cleanser

Citrus fruits stimulate the digestive system. In traditional folk medicine it was thought they also acted as a cleanser and astringent, stimulating the liver and gall bladder.

Serves 1

* (1 pink or ruby grapefruit, zest and a little pith removed, halved) ✳
* 1 orange, zest and a little pith removed, halved
* 1 lime, zest and pith removed from half
* 1 large pear, halved
* small handful of ice (optional) ✳

water
pinch of cinnamon

To make this juice

Feed the grapefruit, orange and lime, then pear through a juicer. Half-fill a glass with ice (if using), pour in the juice and serve immediately.

Pears
to add sweetness

Grapefruit and lime juices can be a little sharp for some tastes, even when mixed with orange juice. Fresh pear juice, which is rich in natural fruit sugars, takes the edge off the sharpness. High in water, pear helps to rehydrate the body. The pectin in pears helps to lower cholesterol and acts as a diuretic and mild laxative.

Grapefruit nutrition

Grapefruit is a great source of vitamin C. It is packed with flavonoids (natural chemical compounds that may reduce early damage to DNA and cell membranes).

Detox

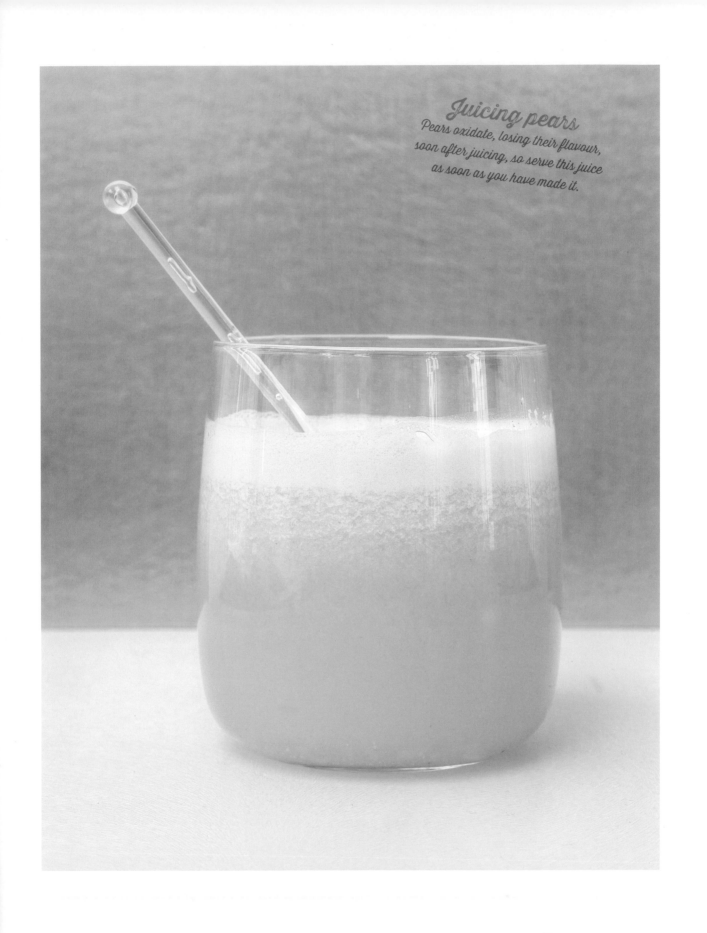

Cucumber spring clean

Think of this as a chilled gingered gazpacho, and you can enjoy the detox qualities of ginger and onion for a light lunch. If you drink it outside in the sunshine you could almost feel transported to a Mediterranean terrace.

Serves 1

* ½ romaine lettuce
* 2 tomatoes
* 2-cm/¾-inch piece of fresh ginger
* 1 spring onion
* 1 celery stick, halved
* 1 carrot, halved
* ¼ cucumber, plus a slice to garnish (optional)
* small handful of ice (optional)

Whizz it up

Feed the lettuce and tomatoes, then ginger, onion, celery, carrot and cucumber through a juicer. Half-fill a glass with ice (if using), pour in the juice, add the cucumber slice to garnish (if using) and serve immediately.

Love your lettuce

Lettuces contain the latex-like compound lactucarium, which is thought to calm and soothe the nerves and aid sleep. They are about 90 per cent water. The outer leaves supply the most beta carotene, vitamin C, folate and iron.

Know your onions

Onions, leeks and garlic are rich in antiviral and antibacterial nutrients that are thought to cleanse the system. They are most potent when eaten raw, but use just a little as they have a strong flavour.

Lettuce choice

If you don't have a romaine lettuce, choose from cos or iceberg. Little gem would also work, but you would need to use two of them.

Green jump-start

If you like spinach or watercress soup, you will love this juice. You don't get a huge amount of juice from these green leaves, but what you do get is concentrated with antioxidants, minerals and vitamins. Mix them with thirst-quenching courgettes and apples for a health boost that will jump-start your detox.

Serves 1

* 55 g/2 oz young spinach
* 30 g/1 oz watercress
* 1 courgette, halved
* 2 apples, halved
* 1 tsp wheatgrass powder (optional)
* small handful of ice (optional)

Give it a whirl

Feed the spinach and watercress, then courgette and apples through a juicer. Stir in the wheatgrass powder (if using). Half-fill a glass with ice (if using), pour in the juice and serve immediately.

Get into good habits

A detox can help you review your eating habits. Most of us don't eat enough green veg, and this tasty juice is a way to increase your consumption easily.

Broccoli & parsley revitalizer

Wonderfully soothing and gentle, this delicate, revitalizing green juice is naturally sweet and refreshing, and makes a perfect alternative to a caffeine-loaded tea or coffee mid-afternoon.

Serves 1

* 115 g/4 oz broccoli, broken into large florets
* small handful of fresh flat-leaf parsley
* ½ fennel bulb
* 2 apples, halved
* chilled water, to taste
* small handful of ice (optional)

Fire up your juicer

Feed the broccoli and parsley, then fennel and apples through a juicer. Top up with water to taste. Half-fill a glass with ice (if using), pour in the juice and serve immediately.

Fabulous fennel

Fennel acts as a diuretic and has a calming effect on the stomach while providing useful amounts of beta carotene and folate. Parsley is also a diuretic and herbalists have long believed it helps reduce inflammation in the kidneys and bladder.

Papaya & apricot soother

Papaya and apricots blend to a wonderfully silky, smooth texture that feels soothing, especially if you are battling a sore throat. This smoothie is packed with vitamin C to help fight off the symptoms of colds and flu.

Serves 1

* ½ papaya, peeled, deseeded and roughly chopped
* 4 apricots, halved and pitted
* 2 oranges, juice squeezed
* 1 lime, juice squeezed
* small handful of crushed ice (optional)
* 4 tbsp chilled water

Mix it up

Put the papaya, apricots and orange and lime juices in a blender and whizz until smooth. Add the crushed ice (if using) and water and whizz again. Pour into a glass and serve immediately.

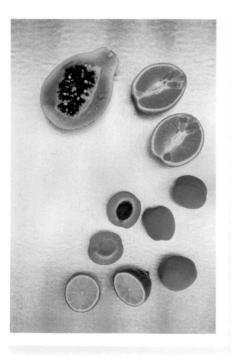

Best drinks for the morning

Serious fans of detoxing diets recommend that you drink fruit juices in the morning, as they believe these have a stronger detoxifying effect than vegetable juices. Fruit juices do have a mild laxative effect – and as the papaya and apricots are blended rather than juiced in this drink, it also contains soluble fibre that will help keep your digestive system moving and expel cholesterol from your body.

Broccoli & parsley revitalizer

page 164

Papaya & apricot soother

page 165

Red cabbage digestive aid

You will be amazed at the vibrant purple juice that comes from a red cabbage. While this drink might look a little like a witch's brew, it is far from wicked. It is light and aromatic, with a hint of cardamom (said to calm digestion) and the delicate sweetness of red grapes.

Serves 1

* 150 g/5½ oz red grapes
* ½ fennel bulb
* ¼ red cabbage, roughly chopped
* 3 cardamom pods
* chilled water, to taste
* small handful of ice (optional)

Time to get started

Feed the grapes, then fennel, then red cabbage through a juicer. Roughly crush the cardamom using a pestle in a mortar, discard the pods and then finely crush the black seeds and stir them into the juice. Top up with water to taste. Half-fill a glass with ice (if using), pour in the juice and serve immediately.

Big apple detox

With its creamy, delicate flavour and cleansing ginger, this juice is perfect for after an indulgent holiday or Christmas.

Serves 1

* 1 parsnip, halved
* 5-mm/¼-inch piece of fresh ginger
* 2 apples, halved
* 125 ml/4 fl oz chilled water
* small handful of ice (optional)

Give it a whirl

Feed the parsnip and ginger, then apples through a juicer. Top up with the water. Half-fill a glass with ice (if using), pour in the juice and serve immediately.

Fresh is best

Instead of buying commercially made detox compounds or potions, freshly juice fruit and vegetables at home. Look at what you eat and when; you might find that making small changes will have a big impact. Ditch that high-calorie, full-fat coffee latte or cola and have a low-calorie, high-vitamin and high-mineral juice instead.

Superfoods: carrots

Studies have shown that a diet rich in carotenoids (the pigment that makes carrots orange) may help lower the risk of heart disease, while the soluble fibre that carrots contain can help lower blood cholesterol. Their high level of beta carotene is converted by the body into vitamin A and helps maintain good eye health and the ability of our eyes to adjust quickly to changes in light. In traditional medicine, carrots were known for their detoxifying properties and for helping to beat acne. For those trying to keep wrinkles at bay, vitamin A is thought to nourish the skin and help fight the signs of ageing; it is even added to some beauty creams! But before you overdose on carrot juice, bear in mind that too many carrots can make your skin turn a little orange.

Grape nutrient-booster

Naturally sweet grapes are a terrific way to disguise the taste of nutritious veg such as cabbage in a juice. As the pumpkin seeds in this drink are finely ground, no one will know they are there either!

Serves 1

* 2 pears, halved
* ¼ small Savoy cabbage, roughly chopped
* 1 tbsp pumpkin seeds
* 150 g/5½ oz green seedless grapes
* small handful of crushed ice (optional)

Whizz it up

Feed the pears and cabbage through a juicer. Put the pumpkin seeds in a blender and whizz until finely ground, then add the grapes and crushed ice (if using) and whizz again. Pour in the pear juice mix and whizz until smooth. Pour into a glass and serve immediately.

Cabbage nutrition

You may have heard about the seven-day cabbage diet to help you detox and shed weight, but you may not know that Savoy cabbage (part of the same family as kale, Brussels sprouts and broccoli) has long been a favourite in herbal remedies. Savoy cabbage is a storehouse of phytochemicals and powerful antioxidants, which are thought to help protect against cancer. It also contains a huge range of vitamins and minerals, not to mention beta carotene and the amino acid glutamine (an anti-inflammatory). Plus it may help to reduce bad cholesterol in the blood.

Seed swap

Don't have any pumpkin seeds? Then add a few sesame or sunflower seeds or a small handful of finely ground almonds instead.

Index